Beaches

HOUGHTON MIFFLIN COMPANY

BOSTON

ATLANTA   DALLAS   GENEVA, ILLINOIS   PALO ALTO   PRINCETON

Beaches

By Jeri Kroll

Illustrated by Mark Wilson

I love rambling beaches,

a sail-studded bay,

sun like a dragon

that no one can slay.

I love tangled seaweed,

the slap of the sea,

foam like a thick shake

sticking to me.

I love, when the tide's out,

to blaze my own trail

from island to rock pool

and fill up my pail.

I find ghostly jellyfish,

crabs, speckled stones,

mother-of-pearl shells,

and white cuttlebones.

In the evening I love

how the salty wind blows.

We pack up our picnic

and put on our clothes.

I bring the beach home,

though.

The best souvenirs

are the sand in my hair

and the waves in my ears.